The Ren & Stimpy Show™

"Seeck Leetle Monkeys"

IS YEAR'S MODEL
DAN SLOTT - script
MIKE KAZALEH - art
ED LAZELLARI - color
BRAD K. JOYCE - letters

THE POACHMAN ALWAYS RINGS TWICE
DAN SLOTT - script
KEN MITCHRONEY - art
ED LAZELLARI - color
LORETTA KROL - letters

U.S. Ohhhhh NO!
DAN SLOTT - script
KEN MITCHRONEY - art
ED LAZELLARI - color
SUE CRESPI - letters

BREAD OVER HEELS
DAN SLOTT - script
MIKE KAZALEH - art
ED LAZELLARI - color
BRAD K. JOYCE - letters

MINIMALIST CHAPTER
DAN SLOTT - script
MIKE KAZALEH - art
ED LAZELLARI - color
BRAD K. JOYCE - letters

LATE NIGHT WITH MUDDY MUDSKIPPER
BARRY DUTTER - plot
MIKE KAZALEH - script & art
BRAD K. JOYCE - letters
ED LAZELLARI - colors

BABY SITTERS
BARRY DUTTER - script
MIKE KAZALEH - art
STEVE DUTRO - letters
ED LAZELLARI - color

MORE GROOVY CREDITS HERE, MAN!
DAWN GEIGER - designer eediot
HERB ASCHERMAN & TOM ROAKE - intern eediots
MIKE LACKEY - reprint eediot
CARL POTTS - eediot in chief

ALSO THANKS TO:
SUSAN LOPUSNIAK, MICHELE JABLONER, WILL McROBB, GWAR, ANNE O'BRIEN, STEVE BUNCHE, CARL POTTS, ROMITA'S RAIDERS : STEVIE, SCUMMY, & RICHIE, "Lethal" LARRY HAMA, CHI, RALF MACCHIO, and TIM TUOHY.

THE REN & STIMPY SHOW™ **SEECK LEETLE MONKEYS.** Originally published in magazine form as the Ren & Stimpy Show #'s 17-20. Published by MARVEL COMICS. OFFICE OF PUBLICATION: 387 PARK AVENUE SOUTH, NEW YORK, N.Y. 10016. THE REN & STIMPY SHOW (including all prominent characters featured in this issue and the distinctive likenesses thereof) is a trademark owned and licensed for use by NICKELODEON, a programming service of Viacom International, Inc., and is used only with permission. All rights reserved. All Ren & Stimpy material Copyright © 1994 Nickelodeon. All rights reserved. All other material Copyright © 1994 Marvel Entertainment Group, Inc. All rights reserved. No part of this book may be printed or reproduced in any manner without the written permission of the publisher. Printed in Canada. ISBN #0-7851-0064-4. First Printing January, 1995. GST #R127032852

10 9 8 7 6 5 4 3 2 1

STIMPSON J. CAT!!

CLAP CLAP CLAP
CLAP CLAP

FIRST OFF...

‡SNIFF SNIFF‡

I WOULD LIKE TO THANK THE LOSERS. FOR WITHOUT THEIR LOSING, I COULD NOT WIN...

SPEED RECORD TROPHY AWARDED TO MARLON BRANDO

@*☆#!!

@*☆#!!

@*☆#!!

@*☆#!!

ALL THAT DIETING FOR NOTHING!

TO THANK MY EXERCISE COACH...

...AND MY PHOTO-RETOUCHER, REN...

...WHO, IN UNISON, GAVE ME SUCH A SMOOTH-LOOKIN' BUTT.

HA!

WHAT A KEEDER!

OH, EET WAS GOIN' GREAT ALL RIGHT! STIMPY HAD HEES MODELLING, AND I HAD MY LUCRATIVE S~~CAM~~...

...UR...UH...I MEAN, MY LUCRATIVE FASHION DESIGNING.

EEF ONLY WE COULD HAVE FORESEEN THE IMPENDING DOOM ON THE HORIZON...

END OF PART ONE!

GO NEKKID!

LOOK, FELLAS, I'M NOT SAYING THAT YOU'RE OLD HAT, BUT YOU'RE KINDA OVER-EXPOSED.

IF YOU WANT TO MAKE THE COVER OF OUR MAGAZINE *AGAIN*, YOU *HAVETA* SHOW THE READERS SOMETHING MORE... ...NEW.

SO WHATCHA SAY? WILL YOU DO IT?

OOOHHH *NO!*

DO WE LOOK LIKE THE KIND OF GUYS WHO'D PARTAKE IN DEGRADING FEELTH OR SMUT?!

NOT US, LADY!

NOT FOR THE KINDA DOUGH YOU'RE OFFERIN'!

THIS ISN'T DEGRADING FILTH OR SMUT. THIS'S ART.

EVERYBODY'S DOING IT: DEMI, SHARON, CINDY, SLY...

WHY HERE'S A NEKKID-SPREAD I DID OF THE *STOOGES.*

CHEEZ!

GOSH!

DO YOU HAVE TROUBLE SLEEPING?

WEEKEND WITH LARRY

HEY! THEES EES *ART!* I'M IMPRESSED!

I NEVER KNEW LARRY HAD THAT MUCH DEPTH!

OR CURLY THAT MUCH GIRTH...

LATE AT NIGHT, A SINISTER FIGURE MAKES HIS WAY ACROSS THE U.S./CANADIAN BORDER...

THEM

U.S.

...ARMED ONLY WITH A POT OF WATER, A CAN OF SALT, AND A SLOTTED SPOON.

HOLD IT RIGHT THERE, MISTER!

NO SUDDEN MOVES!

WE GOTCHA SURROUNDED, EH?

HE'S A SPRY ONE, EH?

WOOSH

AH, JUST AS I SUSPECTED! A POACHER!

THIS CALLS FOR OUR BEST MEN!

SEND OUT THE CALL FOR...

LATER...

HOW MANY TIMES MUST I EXPLAIN THEES TO YOU?

WE ARE DEESGUISING OURSELVES AS "POACHABLES" TO LURE OUR FOE INTO THE OPEN...

SO... UH... REN, WHY ARE YOU DRESSED UP LIKE A GIANT EYE-BOOGER?

I'M AN EGG, YOU FOOL, AN EGG!

AND WHERE EES YOUR DEESGUISE, MAN?

RIGHT HERE, PAL.

FLAP FLAP

BUT THAT'S A LIVE SALMON!

UH HUH.

SPLUTCH

MWURPHH... STOP IT!

NYEEW! I THEENK I'M GONNA BE SEECK!

SPLORTCH

HURRK! OH THE PAIN!!!

HMMM... 47 HOURS, AND STEELL NO SIGN OF HEEM!

GAK

GAK

MMM! MMM! IT HURTS!!

AIM...

BELCH!

KOFF

GAG   KACK

HAKK

OH THE HUMANITY!

ZING ZING ZING

AH!

SO YOU WANT SOME MORE, EH?

ABOUT FACE!

THIS CAT'S JUST PACKED DOWN A THREE-BEAN BURRITO WEETH EXTRA SPICY SALSA!

HIS UNDER LEG NOISES HAVE BEEN CLOCKED AT OVER 100 MPH!

SO JUS' ASK YOURSELVES... DO YOU FEEL LUCKY PUNKS?!

DON'T MESS WEETH ME, MAN!

GNNNN! MUST... HOLD... UP... THE REAR!

ATTENTSHUN!

GOOD WORK, MEN! WE IS ALL PROUD OF YOUSE BOYS!

BUT WE'RE NOT GONNA GIVE YOU NO SHINY MEDALS!

OUR GUY'S HQ.

WE'RE NOT GONNA PROMOTE YAH! AND WE'RE NOT GONNA GIVE YA A RAISE!

WE GOT SOMETHIN' MUCH BETTER IN STORE FOR YOOOOOUUU! WE GOT--

--YOUR VERY OWN U.S.O. SHOW!!!*

STARRIN' THE COMIC STYLINGS OF ME: RIP ROOSTER!

*UNSETTLED SOLDIERS OASIS.

THUSLY--

HEY RIP, HOW MANY LIGHTBULB CHANGERS DOES IT TAKE TO CHANGE A LIGHTBULB?

& HEEZ LEETLE PAL EL POLO LOCO!

I DON'T KNOW, PACO, HOW MANY LIGHTBULB CHANGERS DOES IT TAKE TO CHANGE A LIGHTBULB?

ONE.

TH-TH-THEES EES *HORRIBLE!*

STIMPY! HELP ME, PAL!

BE MY *ROCK!* MY *ANCHOR!* MY *LIFE-LINE* TO SANITY!

L-L-LOOK REN...

HE C-CAN SPIN PLATES ON HIS BEAK *AND* J-J-JUGGLE SCARVES!

S L A P P

SNAP OUT OF EET, MAN!

MUST GET US OUT OF THEES!

EEF ONLY WE HAD SOME KIND OF DEESTRACTION!

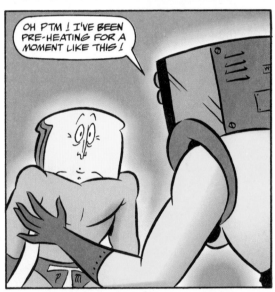

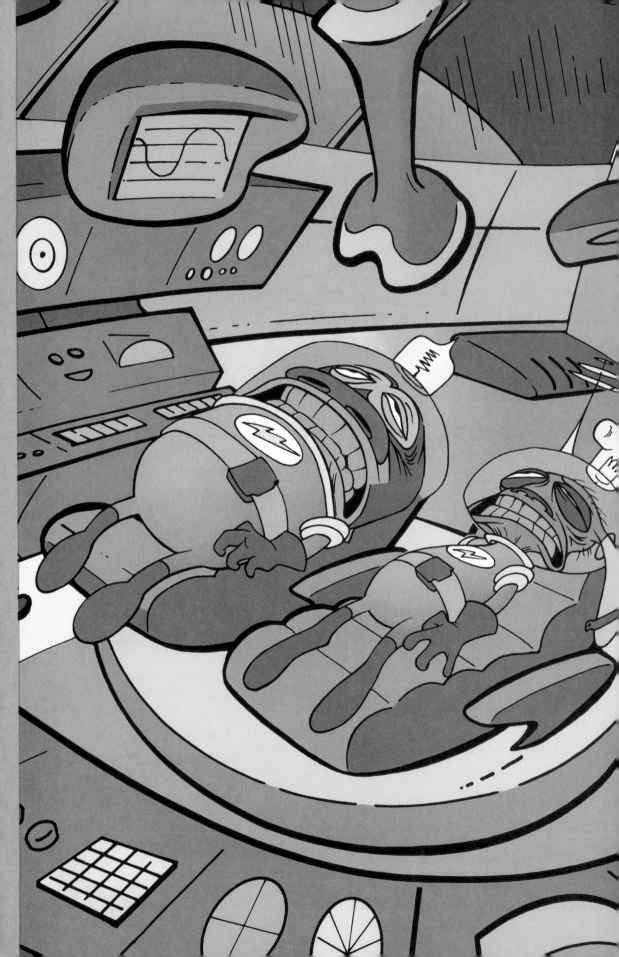

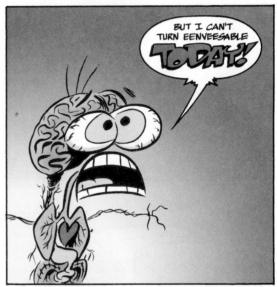

CHAPTER 2

REN & STiMPY ARE "IN THE DARK!"

CHAPTER 4 — **REN HOËK IN** **WAITER CALLED GODOT**

HEY! HOW 'BOUT SOME SERVICE HERE?!

Fin.

LUMP'S activity page

TODAY'S LESSON: HOW TO MAKE

ORIGAMI ROCK

HALLO, KINDER!

STEP ONE

TAKE DA PAPEH...

STEP TWO

...KRUSH DA PAPEH...

STEP THREE

...SEE? ORIGAMI ROCK!

ENJOY!

I'M THE PRODUCER OF THIS SHOW.

WE'VE GOT FOUR MORE SHOWS TO DO THIS WEEK. WITHOUT A HOST, WE'RE *SUNK!*

FEAR NOT. I HAVE A HOST FOR YOU. ONE WEETH A SPARKLEENG PERSONALITY AND WEET!

REALLY? WHO?

ME.

YOU?

LOOK, MAN, THEES SHOW EES EEN THE DOLDRUMS. A FRESH FACE WEEL DO WONDERS!

I'M TALKIN' ABOUT *MY FACE!* EET'S A *BEAUTIFUL FACE!* SIGN ON THE DOTTED LINE, PAL!

Contract

Er, REN? THIS ISN'T USING MY TALENT FOR MY OWN EXPLOITATION, IS IT?

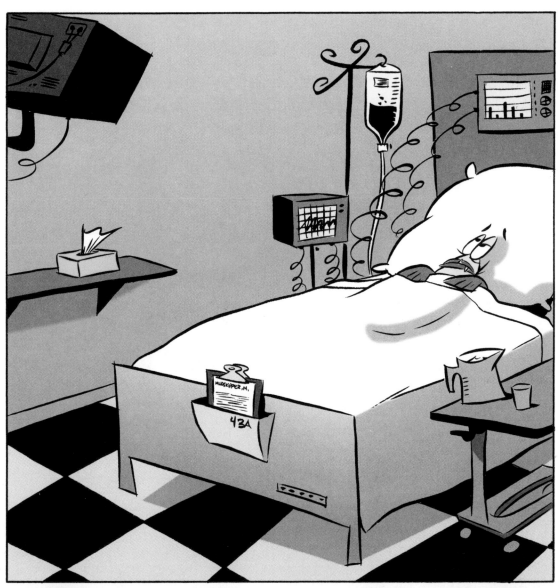

GOOD EVENEENG, LADIES AND GERMS...WELCOME TO THE REN HOËK SHOW.

EET EES CUSTOMARY ON THEES TYPE OF PROGRAM TO START WEETH A VERY FUNNY MONOLOGUE...

ALREADY THERE ARE MEN STANDEENG AROUND THE STUDIO HOLDEENG UP PIECES OF CARDBOARD WEETH JOKES ON THEM FOR ME TO READ.

HAR, Har!

WHOEVER WRITES THEESE JOKES EES A SCREAM! HA HA Ha ha ha!

HAR HAR

...AND THAT ONE OVER THERE EES HEESTERICAL!

23

LOOK HOW I AM READEENG AND LAFFEENG! WHAT *GREAT* JOKES! HA HA HA HA!

SO, STEEMPY, YOU SECOND BANANA-TYPE PERSON, WHO EES OUR FIRST GUEST TONIGHT?

OH, WE'VE GOT A *REAL* GOOD ONE! I WAS LUCKY ENOUGH TO GET "FINGERS" SCHMIDLAPP!

"FEENGERS" Schmidlapp? WHAT ARE YOU, SOME KINDA EEDIOT? WHO EES "FEENGERS" SCHMIDLAPP?

HE OWNS THE GRITTY-KITTY FACTORY IN DES MOINES, IOWA! PLANT NUMBER 23, IN FACT...

WELL, HERE HE EES... ...THE ONE...THE ONLY... "FEENGERS" SCHMIDLAPP!

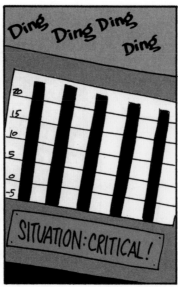

BABY SITTERS!